THE NAVAL FORCES
OF THE
UNITED KINGDOM
1999-2000

Editor - Charles Heyman

Copyright © R & F (Defence Publications)

ISBN 0 85052 687 6

Price £2.50

Pen & Sword Books Ltd
47 Church Street
Barnsley S70 2AS

Telephone : 01226 734222   Fax : 01226 734438

The Information in this publication has been gathered from
unclassified sources.

Front Cover: HMS Illustrious launches an aircraft in the
Arabian Gulf during early 1998.

CONTENTS LIST

Total British Armed Forces	1
Ministry of Defence (MoD)	1
Defence Council	2
Chief of The Defence Staff	2
Chain of Command	2
UK Defence Budget	2
Defence Personnel Totals	3
The Royal Navy	**5**
Royal Naval Summary	5
Composition of the Fleet	5
The Merchant Navy	8
The Admiralty Board	9
Chief of the Naval Staff	9
Royal Naval Chain of Command	11
Fleet Disposition	13
Outline Organisation of a Frigate	15
Royal Naval Shore Establishments	16
Royal Naval Reserve Units	16
Strategic Deterrent	17
Fleet Submarines	18
Aircraft Carriers	20
Assault Ships	22
Type 42 Destroyers	22
Broadsword Class Frigates (Type 22)	23
Duke Class Frigates (Type 23)	24
Common New Generation Frigate	26
Hunt Class (MCMV)	26
Single Role Minehunter	27
Fishery Protection and Offshore Patrol	28
River Class Minesweepers	29
Survey Ships	29
Ice Patrol Ship	31
Training Ships	31
Royal Fleet Auxiliary Service	32
Support Tankers	32
Fleet Replenishment Ships	33
Aviation Training Ship	33
Forward Repair Ship	33
Landing Ships Logistic	34
Ro-Ro General Cargo Ship	34
Royal Maritime Auxiliary Service	34
Fleet Air Arm	35
Sea Harrier	36
Sea King	37

Lynx	38
EH 101 Merlin HAS Mk1	39
Royal Naval Missiles	40
The Royal Marines	41
The Impact of the Strategic Defence Review 1998 (SDR) on the Naval forces of the U.K.	**44**

Total British Armed Forces - Overview (as at 1 April 1998)

Regular: 210,100; Locally Entered 4,000; Regular Reserves 254,700; Volunteer Reserves 62,400; Cadet Forces 127,600; MoD Civilians 119,100 (includes 4,000 locally entered civilians).

Regular Army 109,800; Royal Navy 44,500; Royal Air Force 55,800; (figures include all trained and untrained personnel). Royal Naval figure includes some 6,000 Royal Marines. Planned redundancies will bring the RAF figure down to 52,500 by "the turn of the century".

Strategic Forces
3 x Vanguard Class submarines each with 16 x Trident (D5) Submarine Launched Ballistic Missiles (SLBM). The 4th Vanguard Class submarine with 16 x Trident D5 SLBM probably becoming operational "early in the next century". Future plans are for a stockpile of 200 operationally available warheads and 58 missile bodies.

Royal Navy
44,500: 12 x Tactical Submarines; 3 x Aircraft Carriers; 35 x Destroyers and Frigates; 19 x Mine Counter Measures Vessels; 2 x Assault Ships; 28 x Patrol Craft; 3 x Harrier Squadrons; 12 x Helicopter Squadrons; 3 x Commando Groups: Royal Fleet Auxiliary 2 x Large Fleet Tankers; 3 x Small Fleet Tankers; 3 x Support Tankers; 3 x Fleet Replenishment Ships; 1 x Helicopter Support Ship; 5 x Landing Ships; 1 x Forward Repair Ship.

Merchant Naval Vessels Registered in the UK and Crown Dependencies: 104 x Tankers; 22 x Bulk Carriers; 13 x Specialised Carriers; 27 x Cellular Container Ships; 86 x Ro-Ro Passenger and Cargo Ships; 80 x Other General Cargo Ships; 9 x Passenger Ships; 62 x Tugs.

Royal Air Force
55,900; 6 x Strike/Attack Squadrons; 5 x Offensive Support Squadrons; 6 x Air Defence Squadrons; 3 x Maritime Patrol Squadrons; 5 x Reconnaissance Squadrons; 2 x Airborne Early Warning Squadrons; 14 x Transport, Tankers and Helicopter Squadrons; 2 x Search and Rescue Squadrons; 6 x Surface to Air Missile Squadrons; 5 x Ground Defence Squadrons.

Army
109,800 (excluding some 3,539 Gurkhas); 1 x Corps Headquarters in Germany (ARRC); 1 x Armoured Divisional HQ in Germany; 1 x Operational Divisional HQ in UK ; 3 x Brigade Headquarters in Germany; 17 x Brigade Headquarters in UK; 1 x Airborne Brigade in UK .

National Police Forces: England and Wales 127,222 Scotland 14,390, Northern Ireland 11,600.

Ministry of Defence (MoD)

In 1963, the three independent service ministries were merged to form the present Ministry of Defence (MoD). This large organisation which directly affects the lives of about half a million servicemen, reservists and MoD employed civilians, is controlled by The Secretary of State for Defence who is assisted by three ministers, the Minister of State for the Armed Forces; Minister of State for Defence Procurement and the Parliamentary Under-Secretary of State.

The Secretary of State for Defence chairs The Defence Council. This Defence Council is the body that makes the policy decisions that ensure the three services are run efficiently, and in accordance with the wishes of the government of the day.

Defence Council

The composition of The Defence Council is as follows:

The Secretary of State for Defence
Minister of State (Armed Forces)
Minister of State (Defence Procurement)
Parliamentary Under Secretary of State for Defence
Chief of the Defence Staff
Vice Chief of the Defence Staff
Chief of the Naval Staff and First Sea Lord
Chief of the Air Staff
Chief of the General Staff
Permanent Under-Secretary of State
Chief of Defence Procurement
Chief Scientific Adviser
Second Permanent Under Secretary of State

Chief of The Defence Staff

The Chief of the Defence Staff (CDS) is the officer responsible to the Secretary of State for Defence for the co-ordinated effort of all three fighting services. He has his own Central Staff Organisation and a Vice Chief of the Defence Staff who ranks as number four in the services hierarchy, following the three single service commanders. The current Chief of the Defence Staff is: **General Sir Charles Guthrie GCB LVO OBE ADC Gen**

Chain of Command

The Chief of the Defence Staff (CDS) commands and co-ordinates the activities of the three services through the following chain of command:

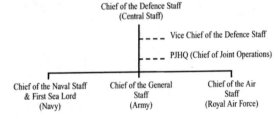

In percentage terms the breakdown of the 1998-99 Defence Budget figure of £22,239.5 million can be shown as follows:

Army TLBs	-	25%
Air Force TLBs	-	18%
Navy TLBs	-	17%
Central TLBs	-	14%
Major Equipment Procurement	-	26%

Defence Personnel Totals
Total Service and Civilian Personnel Strength (1 April 1998)

UK service personnel	210,100
UK civilian personnel	104,200
Locally entered/engaged service personnel	4,000
Locally entered/engaged civilian personnel	15,000
Royal Irish (Home Service)	4,600
	337,900

Strength of UK Regular Forces (1 April 1998)

Royal Navy	Officers	Other Ranks
Trained	6,800	33,600
Untrained	1,000	3,200
Army	**Officers**	**Other Ranks**
Trained	12,700	84,700
Untrained	1,200	11,200
Royal Air Force	**Officers**	**Other Ranks**
Trained	9,900	42,800
Untrained	1,100	2,100

Deployment in Operational Areas (1 April 1998)

Naval Operational Areas	Officers	Other Ranks
Naval Aviation	800	4,000
Fleet Infrastructure	300	900
Surface Fleet	1,100	10,000
Submarines	400	2,700
Royal Marines	500	5,500
	3,100	**23,100**

Army Operational Areas	Officers	Other Ranks
Scotland	200	1,400
2nd Division	800	8,800
London District	400	4,100
4th Division	1,100	12,200
5th Division	400	3,700
1st (UK) Armoured Division	1,200	15,800
UK Support Command (Germany)	700	4,000
3rd UK Division	700	7,500
Reserves & Cadets	-	100
GOC Northern Ireland	800	10,000
Command & Administration	500	400
	6,800	**68,000**
Air Force Operational Areas	**Officers**	**Other Ranks**
1 Group	1,500	12,300

38 Group	1,200	6,200
11/18 Group	1,500	8,600
Directly Administered Units	100	900
Chief of Staff	800	1,400
	5,100	29,400

Overseas Deployment (1 April 1998)

Continental Europe

Royal Navy/Royal Marines	856
Army	23,279
Royal Air Force	4,982
Civilians	1,390

Gibraltar

Royal Navy/Royal Marines	247
Army	103
Royal Air Force	126
Civilians	63

Cyprus

Royal Navy/Royal Marines	5
Army	2,552
Royal Air Force	1,117
Civilians	280

Other Mediterranean, Gulf & Near East

Royal Navy/Royal Marines	1,079
Army	206
Royal Air Force	896
Civilians	12

Far East

Royal Navy/Royal Marines	195
Army	217
Royal Air Force	29
Civilians	26

Other Locations

Royal Navy/Royal Marines	2,839
Army	3,453
Royal Air Force	1,263
Civilians	2,638

Note: These tables include personnel on detachment from units in the UK and the final list (Other Locations) includes personnel on detachment to the Falkland Islands plus Defence Attachès and their military staff.

THE ROYAL NAVY

Royal Naval Summary

Strategic Forces: 3 x Vanguard Class Submarines each equipped with 16 x Trident D5 SLBM (1 more building); 12 x Fleet Submarines; 3 x Aircraft Carriers; 2 x Assault Ships; 12 x Destroyers; 23 x Frigates; 1 x Helicopter Carrier; 19 x Mine Counter Measures Vessels; 24 x Patrol Craft; 1 x Ice Patrol Ship; 7 x Survey Vessels; 3 x Harrier Squadrons; 12 x Helicopter Squadrons; 1 x Marine Bde HQ; 3 x Commando Groups: Royal Fleet Auxiliary 2 x Large Fleet Tankers; 3 x Small Fleet Tankers; 4 x Support Tankers; 5 x Fleet Replenishment Ships; 1 x Aviation Training Ship; 5 x Landing Ships; 1 x Forward Repair Ship; 1 x Ro-Ro Vessel.

The total personnel strength of the Royal Navy at 1 April 1998 was 44,500:

	Trained	Untrained
Officers	6,800	1,000
Other Ranks	33,600	3,100
	40,400	**4,100**

Figures include approximately 6,000 Royal Marines.

Composition of the Fleet

Submarines			Home Base
Trident	3	Vanguard, Victorious, Vigilant.	Faslane
Fleet	7	Tireless, Torbay, Trafalgar Turbulent, Trenchant, Talent, Triumph.	Devonport
	5	Sceptre, Spartan, Splendid, Superb, Sovereign.	Faslane
Carriers	3	Invincible, Illustrious, Ark Royal.	Portsmouth
Destroyers (Type 42)	12	Cardiff, Exeter, Manchester, Newcastle, Nottingham, Southampton, Glasgow, Liverpool, York, Gloucester, Birmingham, Edinburgh.	Portsmouth
Frigates (Type 23)	7	Norfolk, Sutherland, Monmouth, Northumberland, Somerset, Argyll, Montrose.	Devonport
	6	Richmond, Lancaster, Iron Duke, Westminster, Grafton, Marlborough.	Portsmouth

(Type 22)	10	Beaver, Boxer, Brave, Campbeltown, Chatham, Cornwall, London, Coventry, Cumberland, Sheffield.	Devonport
Assault Ships	2	Fearless, Intrepid.	Portsmouth
Helicopter Carrier	1	Ocean.	Devonport (trials)
Offshore Patrol (Castle Class)	2	Dumbarton Castle, Leeds Castle	Portsmouth
(Island Class)	6	Alderney, Guernsey, Anglesey, Lindisfarne, Orkney, Shetland.	Portsmouth
Minehunters (Hunt Class)	13	Berkley, Brocklesby, Chiddingford, Dulverton, Ledbury, Middleton, Quorn, Atherstone, Cattistock, Cottesmore, Hurworth, Brecon, Bicester.	Portsmouth
(Sandown Class)	6	Inverness, Cromer, Sandown, Walney, Bridport, Penzance.	Faslane
River Class	4	Blackwater, Itchen, Spey, Arun. (Being sold to Brazil in late 1998)	Faslane
Patrol Craft	1	Orwell.	Devonport
Costal Training Craft	16	Biter, Blazer, Archer, Charger, Dasher, Smiter, Puncher, Pursuer, Example, Explorer, Express, Exploit, Loyal Watcher, Loyal Chancellor, Tracker, Raider.	

(These 16 vessels are operated by Royal Naval University Training Units).

Search & Rescue Craft	2	Ranger, Trumpeter.	Gibraltar
Ice Patrol	1	Endurance.	Portsmouth
Survey Ships	5	Beagle, Herald, Hecla, Bulldog, Roebuck.	Devonport
	1	Gleaner.	Portsmouth

6

Note: Not all of these ships will be available for operations at any one time and there will always be ships in refit or engaged on trials or training. One of the ASW Carriers is generally in refit and on average 5-7 destroyers/frigates from a total force of 35 will be in refit/standby.

Royal Fleet Auxiliary

Large Fleet Tankers	2	Olna, Olwen.
Small Fleet Tankers	3	Black Rover, Gold Rover, Grey Rover.
Support Tankers	4	Bayleaf, Brambleleaf, Oakleaf, Orangeleaf.
Replenishment Ships	5	Fort George, Fort Austin, Fort Grange, Resource, Fort Victoria.
Aviation Training Ship	1	Argus.
Landing Ship	5	Sir Galahad, Sir Geraint, Sir Bedivere, Sir Percivale, Sir Tristram.
Forward Repair Ship	1	Diligence.
Ro-Ro Cargo Ship	1	Sea Crusader.

Fleet Air Arm

Air Defence Recce/Attack	Sea Harrier F/A2	7	800 Sqn
	Sea Harrier F/A2	7	801 Sqn
	Sea Harrier F/A2	10	899 Sqn
	Harrier T4	4	899 Sqn
Anti-Submarine	Sea King HAS 5/6	12	810 Sqn
	Sea King HAS 5/6	7	814 Sqn
	Sea King HAS 5/6	9	819 Sqn
	Sea King HAS 5/6	7	820 Sqn
Anti-Submarine/ Anti-Ship	Lynx HAS 3, HMA 8	39	815 Sqn (1)
	Lynx HAS 3, HMA 8	12	702 Sqn

Airborne Early Warning	Sea King AEW 2	9	849 Sqn
Commando Assault	Sea King HC4	10	845 Sqn
	Sea King HC4	10	846 Sqn
	Sea King HC4	9	848 Sqn
	Lynx AH7	6	847 Sqn
	Gazelle	9	847 Sqn
Aircrew Training	Jetstream T2	9	750 Sqn
Search & Rescue	Sea King Mk5	5	771 Sqn
Fleet Training & Support	Hawk	12	
	Jetstream T3	2	

Note: (1) This figure includes six aircraft with squadron HQ. The remainder of the aircraft are in flights of one or two aircraft and in the main, on-board ships at sea.

Royal Marines

1 x Commando Brigade Headquarters
1 x Brigade Air Squadron
3 x Royal Marine Commando (Battalion Size)
1 x Commando Regiment Royal Artillery
1 x Commando Artillery Battery (Volunteer)
1 x Commando Squadron Royal Engineers
1 x Commando Squadron Royal Engineers (Volunteer)
1 x Commando Light Helicopter Squadron (847 Sqn)
1 x Commando Logistic Regiment
1 x Special Boat Service Squadrons
2 x Assault Squadrons (Landing Craft)
1 x Security Unit for National Strategic Deterrent

The Merchant Navy

Merchant Naval Vessels Registered in the UK and Crown Dependencies: 106 x Tankers (2,161); 22 x Bulk Carriers (293); 13 x Specialised Carriers (124) ; 26 x Cellular Container Ships (1,017); 86 x Ro-Ro Passenger and Cargo Ships (657) ; 82 x Other General Cargo Ships (145); 9 x Passenger Ships (272); 69 x Tugs.

Note: This listing refers to vessels of 500 gross tons and over. The figures in brackets refer to thousands of gross tons relating to each type of vessel. The total is 4,670 thousand gross tons.

The Admiralty Board

The routine management of the Royal Navy is the responsibility of The Admiralty Board the composition of which is as follows:

The Secretary of State for Defence
Minister of State (Armed Forces)
Minister of State (Defence Procurement)
Parliamentary Under Secretary of State for Defence
Chief of the Naval Staff and First Sea Lord
Commander in Chief Fleet
Second Sea Lord and Commander in Chief Naval Home Command
Second Permanent Under Secretary of State and Secretary of the Admiralty Board
Chief of Fleet Support
Controller of the Navy
Assistant Chief of Naval Staff

Decisions made by The Defence Council or the Admiralty Board are acted upon by the naval staff at the various headquarters throughout the defence chain of command. The First Sea Lord is the officer responsible for the Royal Navy's contribution to the national defence effort and he maintains control through the commander and the staff branches of each of these headquarters.

First Sea Lord and Chief of the Naval Staff
Admiral Sir Michael Boyce KCB OBE ADC

Admiral Sir Michael Boyce joined the Royal Navy in 1962. After completion of basic training he qualified as a Submariner in 1965 and in the next 7 years he served in HM Submarines ANCHORITE, VALIANT and CONQUEROR, also qualifying in this time as a torpedo and anti-submarines specialist. He then completed the Submarine Commanding Officers Qualifying Course in 1973 and subsequently commanded HM Submarines OBERON and OPOSSUM before serving as Staff Warfare Officer to Captain (SM) Submarine Sea Training.

After promotion to Commander in 1976 he attended the Royal Naval Staff Course and from there he joined Flag Officer Submarines Staff as a Staff Warfare Officer. He then commanded HM Submarine SUPERB after which he spent just under a year in the Ministry of Defence (Directorate of Naval Plans) where he was promoted to Captain in 1982. This was followed by command of HMS BRILLIANT and then appointment as Captain (SM) Submarine Sea Training.

In 1986 he returned to the Ministry of Defence to the Directorate of Navy Plans and Programmes as assistant Director (Warfare) and in 1988 he attended the Royal College of Defence Studies. He then served as Senior Naval Officer Middle East in the rank of Commodore before becoming Director of Naval Staff Duties (DNSD) from August 1989 to June 1991.

Admiral Boyce

From DNSD he was promoted Rear Admiral and in July took up the duties of Flag Officer Sea Training and Naval Base Commander Portland. In November 1992, he assumed the duties of Flag Officer Surface Flotilla which, until January 1994, included the NATO appointment of Commander Anti-Submarine Warfare Striking Force.

He was promoted to Vice Admiral in February 1994 and was Knighted in the 1995 New Years Honours List. Promoted to Admiral on 25 May 1995, he simultaneously took up the appointment of Second Sea Lord and Commander-in-Chief Naval Home Command.

On 24 September 1997, Admiral Boyce became Commander-in-Chief Fleet with the accompanying NATO appointments of Commander-in-Chief Eastern Atlantic and Commander Allied Naval Forces Northwestern Europe. On 8 October 1998 he assumed his appointment as First Sea Lord and Chief of Naval Staff and became principal ADC.

Royal Naval Chain of Command

Commander-in-Chief Fleet

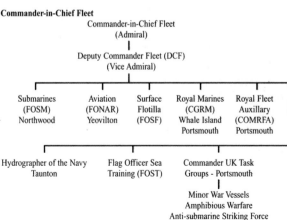

Notes: FOSM - Flag Officer Submarines; FONAR - Flag Officer Naval Aviation; FOSF - Flag Officer Surface Flotilla; CGRM - Commandant General Royal Marines; COMRFA - Commander Royal Fleet Auxilary; FOST - Flag Officer Sea Training.

Naval Home Command

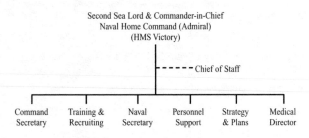

Naval Support Command

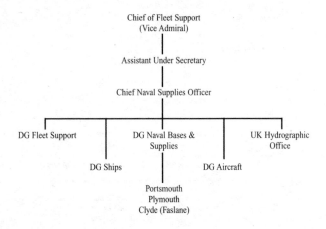

Note: DG's (Director General) is usually a Rear Admiral.

Submarine Flotilla

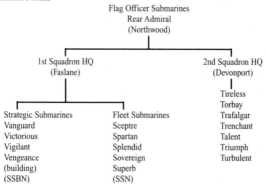

Flag Officer Submarines
Rear Admiral
(Northwood)

1st Squadron HQ
(Faslane)

2nd Squadron HQ
(Devonport)

Tireless
Torbay
Trafalgar
Trenchant
Talent
Triumph
Turbulent

Strategic Submarines
Vanguard
Victorious
Vigilant
Vengeance
(building)
(SSBN)

Fleet Submarines
Sceptre
Spartan
Splendid
Sovereign
Superb
(SSN)

Surface Flotilla

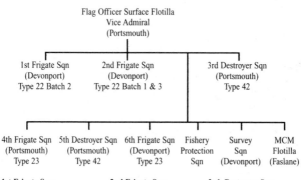

Flag Officer Surface Flotilla
Vice Admiral
(Portsmouth)

1st Frigate Sqn
(Devonport)
Type 22 Batch 2

2nd Frigate Sqn
(Devonport)
Type 22 Batch 1 & 3

3rd Destroyer Sqn
(Portsmouth)
Type 42

4th Frigate Sqn
(Portsmouth)
Type 23

5th Destroyer Sqn
(Portsmouth)
Type 42

6th Frigate Sqn
(Devonport)
Type 23

Fishery
Protection
Sqn

Survey
Sqn
(Devonport)

MCM
Flotilla
(Faslane)

1st Frigate Sqn	**2nd Frigate Sqn**	**3rd Destroyer Sqn**
Boxer	Cornwall	Liverpool
Beaver	Cumberland	Nottingham
Brave	Cambeltown	Glasgow
London	Chatham	Birmingham
Sheffield	Battleaxe	Edinburgh
Coventry		York

13

4th Frigate Sqn	5th Destroyer Sqn	6th Frigate Sqn
Marlborough	Exeter	Montrose
Westminster	Southampton	Norfolk
Iron Duke	Cardiff	Argyll
Lancaster	Newcastle	Northumberland
Richmond	Manchester	Somerset
Grafton	Gloucester	Monmouth
		Sutherland

Mine Counter Measures Flotilla

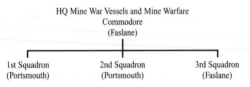

HQ Mine War Vessels and Mine Warfare
Commodore
(Faslane)

| 1st Squadron | 2nd Squadron | 3rd Squadron |
| (Portsmouth) | (Portsmouth) | (Faslane) |

1st Squadron: Middleton, Brocklesby, Ledbury, Chiddingford, Dulverton, Berkley, Quorn.
2nd Squadron: Cattistock, Atherstone, Hurworth, Bicester, Brecon, Cottesmore.
3rd Squadron: Inverness, Bridport, Sandown, Cromer, Walney.

Fishery Protection Squadron
Island Class Offshore Patrol Vessels: Angelsey, Alderney, Guernsey, Shetland, Orkney, Lindisfarne.
Castle Class Offshore Patrol Vessels: Leeds Castle, Dumbarton Castle.

Surveying Squadron
Coastal Survey Vessels: Bulldog, Beagle, Roebuck.
Ocean Survey Ships: Hecla, Herald.
Ice Patrol Ship: Endurance.
Hydrographic Survey Vessel: Gleaner.

Northern Ireland Squadron
River Class MCMV: Itchen, Arun, Spey, Blackwater (these vessels were reported to have been sold to Brazil in late 1998)

1st Patrol Boat Squadron
Archer Class - Fast Training Boats: Blazer, Puncher, Archer, Smiter, Dasher, Pursuer, Charger, Biter, Northella, Loyal Chancellor, Loyal Watcher, Express, Orwell, Example, Explorer, Exploit.

Gibraltar Squadron
Archer Class - Fast Training Boats: Ranger, Trumpeter.
Surveying Flotilla - Headquarters at Devonport

Outline Organisation of a Frigate

The organisation of a typical RN frigate is the result of hundreds of years of evolution and above all, the ship is organised to fight. The four major departments in a modern frigate are the following:

Operations Department - This department basically "fights" the ship and is the direct descendant of the Seaman Branch which manned the guns in earlier generations. There is usually a helicopter embarked and the flight commander reports to the Head of the Operations Department.

Marine Engineering Department - Runs the machinery of the ship ie. the main propulsion units that drive the vessel (gas turbines or diesels), the electrical power supplies and all of the ancillary machinery required.

Weapons Engineering Department - Responsible for the efficient functioning of all of the ship's highly complex sensors and weapons.

Supply Department - Responsible for the logistic arrangements in the ship ie. catering, spares for all of the weapons, general stores, sensors and machinery spares and for all pay and accounting matters.

All of the departments are inter-dependent and each has a head of department - known collectively as "the HODs". These HODs meet at regular intervals and agree such matters as programmes, training and the efficient administration of everything on board. Whilst each HOD is responsible directly to the commanding officer for the efficiency of his department, the Head of the Operations Department generally leads the HODs and is the Second-in-Command - he is known as the First Lieutenant and is a Lieutenant Commander. The other HODs are also likely to be Lieutenant Commanders and, even if senior to the First Lieutenant, are subordinate to him - the First Lieutenant is the man who takes over if the Commanding Officer is unable to perform his duties.

The cleaning of the ship and all of the general tasks are shared by the departments, and the HODs would discuss these matters at their meetings - for example, they would agree how many sailors would be required from each department for a storing at sea operation. A recent development is the presence on board many RN ships of female personnel. These females share all the duties of their male counterparts but, of course, have separate living quarters.

The Commanding Officer is usually a Commander RN (with a background in the Operations Department) and he is known as "The Captain". In command of a squadron of frigates an officer with the rank of Captain RN will be found who doubles the duties both of "Captain" of his ship and Captain (F) to whom the "Captains" of the frigates in his squadron report.

The complement of a frigate relates to the requirement to man the ship for battle. A Batch 3 Type 22 has a total of 232 (13 officers) and a newer Duke Class Type 23 has a complement of 169 (12 officers).

Royal Naval Shore Establishments

HMS Cambridge	Plymouth	Gunnery
HMS Cochrane	Rosyth	Naval Base
HMS Collingwood	Fareham	Weapons Engineering
HMS Daedalus	Lee-on-Solent	Air Engineering & RNAS
Dartmouth BRNC	Dartmouth	Officer Training
HMS Dolphin	Gosport	Submarine Training
HMS Drake	Devonport	Naval Base
HMS Dryad	Fareham	Maritime Operations
HMS Forest Moor	Harrogate	Communications Base
HMS Gannet	Prestwick	RN Air Station
HMS Heron	Yeovilton	RN Air Station
HMS Inskip	Preston	Communications Base
HMS Nelson	Portsmouth	Naval Base
HMS Neptune	Faslane	Submarine Base
HMS Osprey	Portland	RN Air Station (closes 1999)
HMS Raleigh	Torpoint	Training Base
HMS Seahawk	Helston	RNAS Culdrose
HMS Sultan	Gosport	Marine Engineering
HMS Victory	Portsmouth	C-in-C Home Command
HMS Warrior	Northwood	C-in-C Fleet
HMS Excellent	Portsmouth	Operations and Training

Royal Naval Reserve Units

There are Royal Naval Reserve Units located at:

HMS Calliope	Gateshead
HMS Cambria	Penarth
HMS Caroline	Northern Ireland
HMS Dalriada	Greenock
HMS Eaglet	Liverpool
HMS Flying Fox	Bristol
HMS Forward	Birmingham
HMS Northwood	Northwood

HMS President	London
HMS Scotia	Pitreavie
HMS Sherwood	Nottingham
HMS Vivid	Devonport
HMS King Alfred	Portsmouth

The 1998 Strategic Defence Review (SDR) announced that the size of the Royal Naval Reserve will be increased to 3,850. On 1 April 1998, this force consisted of 3,700 personnel.

Strategic Deterrent

The United Kingdom's Strategic Deterrent is operated by the Royal Navy and submarine launched ballistic missiles (SLBM) have been installed in Royal Naval submarines since the late 1960s, with operational patrols commencing in 1969. The first class of SSBN (Nuclear Powered Ballistic Missile Submarine) was the Resolution Class with 4 x vessels of the type:

HMS Resolution	(Commissioned 1967)
HMS Repulse	(Commissioned 1968)
HMS Renown	(Commissioned 1968)
HMS Revenge	(Commissioned 1969)

Resolution Class submarines carried the Polaris 3-TK missile, armed with 6 x 150 kT MRV (Multiple Re-entry Vehicle) warheads. The 3-TK system was believed to have a range of approximately 4,500 km.

The Resolution Class SSBN, have been replaced by the Vanguard Class, and HMS Vanguard, the lead vessel of the class, commenced its first patrol in late 1994/early 1995. The Trident Class submarines, of which there will be four, are armed with 16 x US Trident II D5 missiles and each missile has the capability of carrying up to 12 MIRV (Multiple Independently Targeted Re-entry Vehicle) warheads, making a possible total of 192 warheads per submarine. However, in late 1994, the UK MoD announced that HMS Vanguard would only deploy with a total of 96 UK designed and built A-90 warheads and in general terms, it was believed at the time that in UK service the Trident II D5 will carry eight warheads per missile.

The UK is believed to have purchased 58 x Trident 2D-5 missile bodies from the United States and the range of the missile is believed to be in excess of 9,000 km with a CEP (Circular Error Probable) of about 100 metres.

The second vessel in the class HMS Victorious, reached operational deployment status at the end of 1995 and the third vessel, HMS Vigilant, was ready for operational deployment in early 1997. UK MoD delay in placing the order for the fourth and final vessel of the class (HMS Vengence) means that this submarine will probably be launched in late 1998.

Plans are for at least one of these SSBN to be on patrol constantly and because of their high speed, long endurance underwater, and advanced sensor and electronic equipment, they have little fear of detection.

These large submarines displace over 16,000 tonnes, have a length of 150 metres and the three decks offer accommodation for the crew of 130 which is unusually spacious for a submarine. Good domestic facilities are provided for the crew and the air purification system enables them to remain submerged for long periods without any outside support. Each submarine has two crews known as Port and Starboard; when one crew is away on patrol the other crew is training or taking leave.

Following the 1998 Strategic Defence Review (SDR), the UK MoD revealed that it was no longer necessary to have a stockpile of 300 warheads and that the stockpile was being reduced to 200 operationally available warheads. In addition, the 58 missile bodies already purchased are sufficient to maintain a credible deterrent. The MoD confirmed that there will be one SSBN on patrol at any one time but carrying a reduced load of 48 warheads. The submarine's missiles will not be "targeted" and will be at several days "notice to fire".

Stocks of fissile materials will be reduced. Current (1998) stocks are 7.6 tonnes of plutonium, 21.9 tonnes of highly enriched uranium and 15,000 tonnes of other forms of uranium. The reduction in warheads will allow 0.3 tonnes of weapons-grade plutonium to be placed under international safeguards.

Name	Date Launched
Vanguard	1992
Victorious	1993
Vengeance	1995
Vigilant	1998

Fleet Submarines

The Royal Navy operates two classes of Nuclear Powered Attack Submarines (SSN) as follows:

SWIFTSURE CLASS	Commissioned
Sovereign	1974
Superb	1976
Sceptre	1978
Spartan	1979
Splendid	1981

Dimensions: Length 82.9m; Beam 9.8m; Draught 8.2m; Displacement 4,200 tons surfaced and 4,500 tons dived; Propulsion - 1 x Rolls Royce pressurised water-cooled reactor supplying steam to two sets of General Electric geared turbines delivering 15,000 shp to one shaft; Performance - Max Speed 20 kts surfaced and 30+ kts dived; diving depth 400m (operational) and 600m maximum; Complement 12 officers and 85 ratings; Torpedoes - 5 x 533 mm (21") tubes for 20 x Mk 24 Tigerfish wire-guided and Mk 8 anti-ship torpedoes; Mines - up to 50 x Mk 5 Stonefish or Mk 6 Sea Urchins instead of torpedoes; Missiles - 5 x UGM-84A Sub Harpoon tube-launched anti-ship missiles.

TRAFALGAR CLASS	Commissioned
Trafalgar	1983
Turbulent	1984
Tireless	1985
Torbay	1987
Trenchant	1989
Talent	1990
Triumph	1991

Dimensions: Length 85.4m; Beam 9.8m; Draught 8.2m; Displacement 4,700 tons surfaced and 5,200 tons dived; Propulsion - 1 x Rolls Royce pressurised water-cooled reactor supplying steam to two sets of General Electric geared turbines delivering 15,000 shp to one shaft; Performance - Max Speed 20 kts surfaced and 32 kts dived; diving depth 400m (operational) and 600m maximum; Complement 12 officers and 85 ratings; Torpedoes - 5 x 533mm (21") tubes for 20 x Mk 24 Tigerfish wire-guided and Mk 8 anti-ship torpedoes; Mines - up to 50 x Mk 5 Stonefish or Mk 6 Sea Urchins instead of torpedoes; Missiles - 5 x UGM-84A Sub Harpoon tube-launched anti-ship missiles.

These nuclear-powered fleet submarines are armed with homing torpedoes (range approx 15km+) that can be used against other submarines or surface vessels. The Sub Harpoon long-range anti-ship missile (range 110 km) is now in service as the principal anti-surface ship weapon in these submarines.

Both classes are capable of continuous patrols at high underwater speed, independent of base support, and can circumnavigate the globe without surfacing. Their long endurance and sophisticated weapon systems make them formidable adversaries. There are three decks and although space is restricted, living conditions are comfortable.

In 1995, the UK MoD announced that total of seven in-service SSNs (two Swiftsure class and five Trafalgar class) will be modified for the Tomahawk cruise missile. By 2003, the RN aims to have five TLAM-capable boats fully operational at any one time. The UK is acquiring an initial 65 Tomahawk Block III missiles built by Hughes Missile Systems Company under a US Foreign Military Sales (FMS) agreement worth £180 million.

Under the terms of the 1998 SDR it was announced that the nuclear-powered attack submarine force would be reduced from 12 to 10 "in the longer term" but that all 10 submarines would now be fitted with the Tomahawk land attack cruise missile. The Tomahawk TLAM-C (Tactical Land Attack Missile - Conventional) has a range of about 950 km.

HMS Splendid began a six-month Capability Upgrade Period (CUP) in October 1997 designed to allow the submarine to operate Tomahawk Land Attack Cruise Missile. The CUP package, the first of its kind, will enable Splendid to conduct the RN's first live firing of TLAM at a Pacific test range off San Diego in November 1998.

In June 1997, the MoD awarded GEC-Marconi a contract worth approximately £2 billion for its VSEL shipbuilding subsidiary to build the first 3 Astute Class nuclear-powered attack submarines for the Royal Navy. These initial vessels, in the past referred to as the Batch 2 Trafalgar Class, will enter service from 2005 to replace the oldest of the five Swiftsure-class boats that were commissioned between 1974 and 1981. The MoD plans to order a further two Astute-class SSNs after 2000 to succeed the remaining Swiftsure Class submarines.

The 6,000-tonne Astute Class SSNs will be faster and quieter than the Trafalgar Class boats, and their PWR-2 nuclear reactors will not require refuelling over the 25 to 30 years that the vessels will be in service. Each will carry a total of 36 weapons - a mix of Spearfish heavyweight torpedoes, Harpoon anti-ship missiles, and Tomahawk TLAC-M.

Aircraft Carriers

The Royal Navy operates 3 x Aircraft/ASW Carriers of which two are generally available and one is in refit at any one time: These vessels are:

	Commissioned
Invincible	1980
Illustrious	1982
Ark Royal	1985

Major Characteristics - Speed 28 knots; Displacement 16,800 tons (standard) 19,000 (full load); Engines 4 x Rolls Royce Olympus TM3B Gas Turbines delivering 112,000 shp to two shafts; Length 206.6m; Beam 27.5m; Draught 7.3m; Flight Deck Length 167.8m; Complement 131 officers and 870 rates plus an air group of 320.

The primary task of this class of ship is to act as the command ship of anti-submarine warfare forces. They are also effective and flexible command ships for air operations and aircraft from the carriers Invincible and Illustrious were involved in operations in the former Yugoslavia during 1995 and more recently, in the Persian Gulf during late 1997 - early 1998.

All three carriers carry Sea King anti-submarine (ASW) helicopters, Sea King airborne early warning (AEW) helicopters and Sea Harrier aircraft. A typical embarked "air group" could consist of:

> 8 x Sea Harriers
> 8 x Sea King HAS.6 (ASW)
> 3 x Sea King HAS.2 (AEW)

Note: During the past three years RAF Chinook helicopters have been conducting deck trials on HMS Invincible and HMS Illustrious.

The Sea Dart medium-range surface-to-air missile is fitted for air defence (with a secondary anti-ship role) and the Phalanx or Goalkeeper rapid-firing gun systems have been fitted to enhance the close-range anti-missile defence capability. A 'ski-jump' launching ramp is fitted to improve the operational take-off performance of the Sea Harrier. The vessels are powered by Rolls-Royce Olympus gas-turbine engines and on average these ships took approximately 6-7 years to build.

Following the 1998 SDR, the UK MoD announced its intention to replace the current carrier force with two larger vessels once these vessels have reached the end of their planned life. The statement in the SDR reads "Work will now begin to refine our requirements but present thinking suggests that they may be of the order of 30,000-40,000 tonnes and capable of deploying up to 50 aircraft, including helicopters. Our intention is that they will be built using all of the relevant cost-saving techniques, following the example of HMS Ocean. No decisions have been taken on a future carrier-borne aircraft but a version of the Joint Strike Fighter currently in development in the United States remains a strong contender. We are therefore participating in the concept demonstration phase of this programme."

The UK MoD is known to have been looking at replacement vessels due for service around 2010-2015 for some time and three study teams directed by a Studies Steering Group have been commissioned. These three study groups are believed to be looking at three differing platform designs. The first is a design catering for Conventional Take Off and Landing (CTOL) aircraft, the second would operate aircraft of the Short Take Off and Arrested Recovery (STOBAR) type and the third would operate Advanced Short Take-Off and Vertical Landing (ASTOVL) aircraft.

In the interim, HMS Ocean, an LPH (Landing Platform Helicopter) has been launched and is undergoing trials prior to joining the fleet. The hull of the ship is being built to Merchant Navy standards at a cost of some £170 million. The ship should be able to carry an air group of 12 x Sea King HAS.4 troop lift helicopters and 6 x Lynx HAS.8 attack helicopters (although these could be replaced by EH 101 and Apache by the end of the decade). Current plans are for HMS Ocean to have a crew of 250 and the ship will be capable of carrying a complete Marine Commando (up to 850 personnel).

Assault Ships

Major Characteristics - Speed 21 knots; Displacement 11,582 tons; Engines 2 x sets of English Electric geared steam turbines delivering 22,000 shp to 2 props; Length 158m; Beam 24.3m; Draught 6.2m; Complement 50 officers and 50 rates plus air group of 3 officers and 85 rates.

	Commissioned
Fearless	1965
Intrepid	1967

These two vessels are the UK's most versatile vessels for amphibious warfare and proved their worth in the Falklands Campaign. Each is fitted out as a Naval Assault Group/Brigade HQ from which naval and military personnel, working in close co-operation, can mount and control an amphibious operation.

Both ships can transport a military force complete with full supporting armour. 4 x Mk 4 Landing craft capable of transporting 35 troops or a 5.5 ton vehicle are carried in davits and the well deck can carry 2 main battle tanks or 100 tons of stores and 4 x LCM (landing craft). Four more main battle tanks can be carried on the tank deck. The ships can also operate a flight of 4 helicopters and are armed with modern close-range guns for air defence. HMS Fearless is fitted with the Phalanx close-in weapon system to enhance the air defence. In an emergency, the ships could carry up to 1,000 troops. HMS Intrepid is currently in reserve.

Replacements are planned for both HMS Fearless and HMS Intrepid. In a July1996 order to VSEL worth £450 million two replacement vessels were ordered. These vessels, carrying the names of Albion and Bulwark are scheduled to enter service in 2001 and 2003 respectively.

The new ships will be 171 metres in length, displacing 15,000 tons and diesel propulsion will give a top speed of 18 knots. There will be 2 flight deck places for EH 101 helicopters, 4 x LCU landing craft in the well deck and another 5 x landing craft in davits. The crew will total some 325 and 650 embarked troops will be carried.

Type 42 Destroyers

There are currently 12 x Type 42 Guided Missile Destroyers (DDG) whose primary role is to provide air defence for naval task group operations.

	Commissioned
Birmingham	1976 Batch 1
Cardiff	1979 Batch 1
Newcastle	1978 Batch 1
Glasgow	1979 Batch 1
Exeter	1980 Batch 2

Southampton	1981 Batch 2
Nottingham	1982 Batch 2
Liverpool	1982 Batch 2
Manchester	1982 Batch 3
Gloucester	1985 Batch 3
Edinburgh	1985 Batch 3
York	1985 Batch 3

Major Characteristics - Speed 29 knots on Olympus turbines or 18knots on Tyne turbines; Range 7,400 kms at 18 kts; Displacement Batch 1 & 2 - 4,350 full load and Batch 3 - 5,350 at full load; Engines - COGOG Type system with 2 x Rolls Royce Olympus TM3B gas turbines delivering 56,000 shp and 2 x Rolls Royce Tyne RM1A gas turbines delivering 8,500 shp to two shafts; Length 125.6m Batch 1 & 2 and 141.1m for Batch 3; Beam 14.3m Batch 1 & 2 and 14.9m Batch 3; Draught 5.8m; Complement 24 officers and 229 rates (max total 312); Aircraft Carried - Sea Lynx with Sea Skua and or Stingray torpedoes.

In general, these vessels are armed with the Sea Dart medium-range air-defence missile system, which also has an anti-ship capability (1 x Twin Launcher for 24 Sea Dart SAM for Batch 1 & 2 with Batch 3 carrying 40 missiles). The automatic rapid-fire 114mm (4.5 inch) gun with a range of 21 km, anti-submarine torpedo tubes and the Phalanx rapid-firing gun system for close-range anti-missile defence. They also carry the high-speed multi purpose Lynx helicopter armed with anti-submarine weapons and the Sea Skua anti-ship missile which is controlled by the Sea Spray search radar. The latest communication and sensor equipment is fitted in all Type 42 Destroyers.

All the Type 42 Destroyers are based at Portsmouth.

Broadsword Class Frigates (Type 22)

From 1 January 1998, it would appear that the Royal Navy will be operating 10 x Type 22 Frigates whose primary role is anti-submarine warfare:

	Commissioned
Boxer	1983 Batch 2
Beaver	1984 Batch 2

Brave	1986 Batch 2
London	1987 Batch 2
Sheffield	1988 Batch 2
Coventry	1988 Batch 2
Cornwall	1988 Batch 3
Cumberland	1988 Batch 3
Campbeltown	1989 Batch 3
Chatham	1989 Batch 3

The Batch 1 ships, HMS Broadsword, Battleaxe, Brilliant and Brazen, all commissioned between 1979 and 1982 were sold to the Brazilian Navy between 1995 and 97.

Major Characteristics - Speed 30 kts+ on Olympus turbines or 18 knots on Tyne turbines; Range 8,370 km at 18 kts; Displacement 4,600 full load; Engines - COGOG Type system with 2 x Rolls Royce Spey SM1A gas turbines delivering 18,770 shp and 2 x Rolls Royce Tyne RM1A gas turbines delivering 8,500 shp to two shafts; Length 143.6m; Beam 14.8m; Draught 6.0m; Complement 23 officers and 302 rates; Aircraft Carried - 1 or 2 Sea Lynx with Sea Skua and or Stingray torpedoes or 1 x Sea King HAS.6.

Type 22 Frigates of both Batch 2 and Batch 3 are capable of not only anti-submarine operations (their primary role) but anti-aircraft and anti-ship roles. Equipped with the latest computer-assisted sonar systems and communications equipment these vessels are highly efficient maritime hunters. Two Lynx anti-submarine helicopters can be carried and anti-submarine torpedo tubes are fitted. Batch 2 vessels carry the Exocet MM38 surface-to-surface missile (range 65 km) and the Batch 3 vessels the Harpoon surface to surface missile (range 110 km). Sea Wolf close-range air-defence missile systems provide an all-round defence capability and the 30mm Goalkeeper gives defence against incoming missiles. The automatic rapid-fire Vickers Mk 8 DP 114mm (4.5-inch) gun with a range of 21 km is fitted to the batch 3 ships.

All the ships have controllable-pitch propellers and stabilisers. This class is the first in the Royal Navy to be designed to the metric system.

Duke Class Frigates (Type 23)
Although designed for anti-submarine operations, like most new surface combatants of this size, this is really a multi purpose vessel. There are currently 13 ships of this class in service, with another three building.

	Commissioned
Norfolk	1990
Argyll	1991
Marlborough	1991
Lancaster	1991
Iron Duke	1992
Monmouth	1993
Montrose	1993
Westminster	1993
Northumberland	1994
Richmond	1994
Somerset	1996
Grafton	1997
Sutherland	1997
Kent	building (2000)
St Albans	building (2000)
Portland	building (2001)

Major Characteristics - Speed 28 kts+; Range 14,400 km at 15 knots; Displacement 3,500 tons standard; Engines - CODLAG Type system with 2 x Rolls Royce Spey SM1A gas turbines delivering 18,770 shp each; for vessels after HMS Westminster (1994) 2 x Rolls Royce Spey SM1C delivering 26,150 shp each; Length 133m; Beam 16.2m; Draught 5.5m; Complement 12 officers and 157 rates; Aircraft carried - 1 x Sea Lynx with Sea Skua and or Stingray torpedoes.

Designed primarily for the anti-submarine (ASW) role, and fitted with the latest radar and communications systems and towed array sonar. Air defence is provided with a vertical launch Sea Wolf system and the surface armament includes the Harpoon missile system (range 110 km) and the 114mm (4.5-inch) gun for naval gun fire support. From 1998, the Lynx helicopter was replaced by the new 'EH 101 Merlin' helicopter. HMS Norfolk, the first of this class, was commissioned in 1990, the latest to be accepted into service being HMS Sutherland in 1997. Three more have been ordered and will be named HMS Kent, HMS St Albans and HMS Portland. These ships are powered by a CODLAG system (Combined diesel-electric and gas-turbine propulsion) and the diesel-electric is used for minimum underwater noise during ASW operations. This class will form the backbone of the frigate fleet in the short to medium term.

Common New-Generation Frigate (Project HORIZON)

Project HORIZON is a collaborative programme between the UK, France and Italy to procure a new class of Anti-Air Warfare (AAW) frigate. This frigate will replace the UK's existing Type 42 AAW Destroyer and we believe that it would be unrealistic to expect to see this vessel in service before the early part of the next decade.

The Staff Requirement was endorsed in its original form in 1991 as a basis for collaborative negotiations with France following collapse of the NATO AAW frigate project NFR 90. Italy was offered observer status but expressed no active interest until the Autumn of 1992, by which time France and the UK were very close to agreement on a joint Staff Requirement. Italy decided to exercise its option to join with the UK and France to sign a Tripartite Staff Requirement in December 1992.

Collaboration will start with an initial design and validation phase and then proceed to the detailed design and build of three First of Class (FOC) ships. Industry will be encouraged to identify savings arising from common support. Development of the whole ship, including construction of the three FOC ships and the physical integration of the combat system will be contracted to a French - Italian - UK joint venture company. A consortium led by GEC (with BAe and others) was selected in January 1994 as the UK member of the joint venture company.

A Joint Project Office has been established in London with full centralised authority for technical, financial and contractual functions. As host nation, the UK provides the necessary contractual and financial infrastructure.

Combat Management Systems (CMS) project definition (PD) for the project started in March 1996 - about 20 months later than expected. Original plans were for the UK to procure 12 vessels at the rate of 2 per year starting in 2002. However, the project appears to be running about 4 years late and, should it proceed to the production phase, the first UK vessel may be called HMS Daring.

The 1998 SDR states that the MoD plans to modernise the destroyer and frigate force with a new class of Common New Generation Frigates but reduce the overall strength from 35 vessels to 32 (based on concurrent medium scale deployments).

Hunt Class - Mine Counter Measures Vessels (MCMV)

	Commissioned		Commissioned
Brecon	1979	Chiddingford	1984
Ledbury	1981	Hurworth	1985
Cattistock	1982	Bicester	1986
Cottesmore	1983	Atherstone	1987
Brocklesby	1982	Berkley	1987
Middleton	1984	Quorn	1989
Dulverton	1983		

Major Characteristics - Speed 17 knots+; Dispacement 625 tons standard; Engines 2 x Rushton Paxman Deltic 9-59K Diesels; Length 57m; Beam 10m; Draught 2.2m; Complement 6 officers and 39 rates:

The first of this advanced class of GRP-built mine countermeasures vessels, HMS Brecon, entered service in 1979, 13 are now in service, and are due a mid-life update starting in 2000. They are equipped with Remote Control Mine Disposal System (RCMDS) and are fitted with Influence Sweeps and a 30mm gun.

Single Role Minehunter

	Commissioned		
Sandown	1989	Grimsby	Launched 1998
Inverness	1991	Bangor	Building (20000
Cromer	1991	Ramsey	Building (2000)
Walney	1993	Blyth	Building (2001)
Bridport	1993	Shoreham	Building (2001)
Penzance	1997		
Pembroke	Launched 1997		

Major Characteristics - Speed 15 knots+; Displacement 378 tons lights; Engines 2 x Paxman Valentia 6RPA 200-EM 1500 Diesels; Range 2,600 km at 11 knots; Length 52.7m; Beam 10.5m; Draught 2.30m; Complement 5 officers and 29 rates:

HMS Sandown, the first of the new Single-Role Minehunter class entered service in 1989, and HMS Penzance, the latest, entered service in 1997. They are built of GRP, capable of operating in deep and exposed waters and complement the Hunt Class MCMVs. Sandown Class vessels are equipped with a minehunting sonar and mine disposal equipment making them capable of dealing with mines at depths of up to 200m. Each ship carries 2 x Mk2 Remote Control Mine Disposal Systems (Submersibles) capable of identifying and disposing of mines up to 300m depth. 1 x 30mm Oerlikon gun is carried for local defence. When the final order for HMS Shoreham is completed in 2001 there will be 12 vessels of this class in service.

Fishery Protection and Offshore Patrol Vessels

Fishery protection and patrolling Britain's offshore gas and oilfield installations is carried out by the Royal Navy's Fishery Protection Squadron.

Island Class

	Commissioned
Alderney	1979
Guernsey	1977
Anglesey	1979
Lindisfarne	1978
Orkney	1977
Shetland	1977

Major Characteristics - Speed 16.5 knots+; Displacement 998 tons standard; Engines 2 x Rushton 12 RK 3CM Diesels; Range 11,000 kms at 12 knots; Length 61m; Beam 11m; Draught 4.27m; Complement 5 officers and 29 rates:

Six Island Class patrol vessels form the Offshore Division which, in addition to their fishery protection tasks outside the 12-mile coastal limit, carry out regular surveillance patrols of the offshore gas and oilfield installations. The vessels are armed with 1 x 40mm Bofors AA Gun.

Castle Class

	Commissioned
Leeds Castle	1981
Dumbarton Castle	1982

Major Characteristics - Speed 20 knots; Displacement 1,350 tons standard; Engines 2 x Rushton 12 RK 320DM Diesels; Range 10,000 km at 12 knots; Length 81m; Beam 11.5m; Draught 3.42m; Complement 6 officers and 39 rates plus 25 Royal Marines as required.

The two Castle Class patrol vessels which are in service with the Offshore Division have a landing deck and fuelling facilities for the Sea King helicopter. Armament consists of 1 x 30mm Oerlikon and 2 x 7.62mm MG. One of these vessels is generally on patrol around the area of the Falkland Islands.

River Class Minesweepers

Major Characteristics - Speed 14 knots+ ; Displacement 630 tons standard; Engines 2 x Rushton 6 RKCM Diesels; Range 4,500km at 10 knots; Length 47.6m; Beam 10.5m; Draught 3.10m; Complement 7 officers and 23 rates; Armament 1 x 40mm Bofors AA - 2 x 7.62mm MG.

The Northern Ireland Squadron consists of River Class minesweepers, HMS Blackwater, Arun, Itchen and Spey. The primary task of these vessels is to deter the movement of arms, munitions and personnel of the various terrorist factions that exist within the province. These four vessels were commissioned in 1984/85 and are the survivors of a class that originally totalled 12. There were reports in early 1998 that these vessels would be sold to Brazil by the end of the year.

Survey Ships

	Commissioned	
Hecla	1965	Ocean Survey
Herald	1974	Ocean Survey

Major Characteristics - Speed 14 knots+; Displacement 2,510 tons standard; Engines 3 x Paxman Ventura 12YJCZ Diesels; Range 12,000 km at 11 knots; Length 79.3m; Beam 14.9m; Draught 4.0m; Complement 12 officers and 116 rates.

Note: Characteristics relate to HMS Herald which is an improved Hecla Class vessel.

Beagle	1968	Coastal Survey Vessels
Bulldog	1968	Coastal Survey Vessels

Major Characteristics - Speed 15 knots ; Displacement 800 tons standard; Engines 4 x Lister Blackstone ERS-8-M Diesels; Range 4,600 km at 12 knots; Length 60.9m; Beam 11.43; Draught 3.6m; Complement 5 officers and 34 rates.

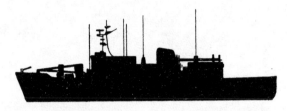

Roebuck	1986	Coastal Survey Vessels

Major Characteristics - Speed 15 knots ; Displacement 1,059 tons standard; Engines 4 x Mirrles ES-8 Mk 1 Diesels; Range 4,000 km at 10 knots; Length 63.8m; Beam 13m; Draught 3.65m; Complement 8 officers and 34 rates.

Gleaner	1983	Surveying Motor Vessel

Major Characteristics - Speed 14 kts ; Displacement 20 tons standard; Length 14.8m; Complement 1 officer and 4 rates.

The Royal Navy's Surveying Service has been operating throughout the world since the formation of the Hydrographic Department in 1795 and the information from oceanographic surveys is used for producing Admiralty charts and nautical publications which have a world wide sale and are used by ships of many nations.

The Surveying Flotilla consists of ocean-going ships, coastal vessels and inshore craft. In addition to surveying in overseas areas, many of the flotilla are constantly engaged in updating the charts covering the waters around the United Kingdom.

To carry out these wide-ranging tasks the latest surveying techniques are employed, including digitised echo-sounders, side scan sonar, automated plotting and recording of position, depth, gravity and magnetic parameters. Satellite and inertial navigation systems are used when out of range of shore-based position fixing systems.

Ice Patrol Ship

Major Characteristics - Speed 12 knots ; Displacement 6,500 tons standard; Engines 2 x Ulstein Bergen BRM-8 Diesels; Range 5,000 km at 12 knots; Length 91m; Beam 17.9m; Draught 6.5m; Complement 15 officers and 97 rates and 15 Royal Marines.

In service with the Royal Navy since 1990, HMS Endurance (previously MV Polar Circle) supports British interests in the South Atlantic and Antarctic waters, working alongside members of the British Antarctic Survey Team, carrying out hydrographic surveying, meteorological work and research programmes. It has a flight deck and hangar for Lynx helicopters. The hull is painted red for easy recognition in the ice.

Training Vessels

Major Characteristics - Speed 22.5 knots ; Displacement 44 tons standard; Engines Perkins CVM 800T Diesels; Range 500 km at 15 knots; Length 20.8m; Beam 5.8m; Draught 1.8m; Complement 11-15 total; Armament 1 x 20mm AA Gun and 2 x 7.62mm MG (Ranger and Trumpeter only).

	Commissioned		Commisssioned
Archer	1985	Puncher	1988
Biter	1985	Charger	1988
Smiter	1985	Ranger	1988
Pursuer	1985	Trumpeter	1988
Blazer	1988	Example	1985
Dasher	1988	Explorer	1985
Exploit	1988	Express	1988

Fourteen Fast Training Boats are in service with the Inshore Training Squadron (ITS) based at Rosyth. The Archer and Example Class supported by the Fleet Tenders Loyal Watcher and Loyal Chancellor are mainly used as University Training Ships. HMS Ranger and Trumpeter are used as Gibraltar Search and Rescue Craft.

Royal Fleet Auxiliary Service

The Royal Navy describes the Royal Fleet Auxiliary Service as "The specialist front-line support force for the Royal Navy that replenishes warships at sea with fuel, stores and weapons. The service is unique in that all the Royal Navy's major Auxiliaries are civilian manned. The RFA service is part of the Royal Naval Supply and Transport Service and employs some 2,500 officers and ratings, who follow the traditional paths of the Merchant Navy to obtain their basic qualifications, with a substantial overlay of Royal Naval training to develop the skills needed in an operational environment. The 22 ships of the Fleet include both large and small Fleet Tankers, Support Tankers, Landing Ships Logistic, an Aviation Training Ship and a Forward Repair ship. Since it was formed in 1905, the RFA service has pioneered and perfected the art of Replenishment at Sea (RAS). RFA vessels are now fitted with close range small-calibre self-defence weapons and decoys which are manned and maintained by RFA personnel".

Fleet Tankers

	In-Service
Olwen	1965
Olna	1966
Grey Rover	1970
Gold Rover	1974
Black Rover	1974

RFAs Olwen and Olna are purpose-built fast Fleet Tankers capable of supporting Naval task groups in the front line with fuel, lubricants and a limited range of stores. The ability of each of these vessels is further enhanced by the provisions of facilities to embark and operate the Royal Navy's ASW Sea King and Lynx helicopters. Both ships are capable of speeds of up to 20 knots carrying 18,000 tons of fuel oil, 1,720 tons of diesel, 3,730 tons of aircraft fuel and 130 tons of lube oil.

There are also three small Fleet Tankers of the Rover Class. These relatively fast and highly manoeuvrable vessels are able to replenish warships with fuel and a limited amount of dry cargo and refrigerated stores. Although they do not normally carry their own helicopter, they are fitted with a flight deck, but no hangar, and are capable of providing a forward operating base for deploying helicopters if they require fuel. Rover Class tankers can carry 7,460 cubic metres of fuel; 326 cubic metres of water; 70 cubic metres of lube oil and 600 cubic metres of aviation fuel or gasoline at a sustained speed of 17 knots.

Support Tankers

	In Service
Brambleleaf	1980
Orangeleaf	1982
Bayleaf	1982
Oakleaf	1981

In general the Royal Navy's Support Tankers have the dual role of replenishing warships and fleet tankers at sea and the bulk movement of fuels between naval supply depots. Expect RFA Oakleaf to be able to carry 43,020 cubic metres of fuel in 16 tanks and the remaining three (Appleleaf Class) tankers approximately 35,000 cubic metres of fuel in 24 tanks. RFA Oakleaf has a crew of 36 and the other three vessels about 65 in total.

Fleet Replenishment Ships

	In Service
Resource	1967
Fort Grange	1978
Fort Austin	1979

RFA Resource is an ammunition, food and stores ship currently believed to be operating at Spit in Croatia in support of United Nations Forces. The ship has seven holds and displaces 22,800 tons. There is a crew of 134 Royal Fleet Auxiliary and 37 civilian staff.

Fort Victoria and Fort George are also ammunition, food and stores ships both capable of operating up to five Sea King helicopters with full maintenance facilities on board. Displacing 22,749 tons and capable of carrying about 12,000 cubic metres in four holds, including 2,300 cubic metres of refrigerated stores, both these ships have a crew of 127 RFA, 36 civilian staff and 45 Royal Naval personnel.

Aviation Training Ship

	In Service
RFA Argus	1981

RFA Argus was launched in 1981 and was formerly the container ship MV Contender Bezant. In 1982, the vessel was used as an aircraft transport during the Falklands War and was purchased by the Royal Navy during 1984. The ship operates Lynx and Sea King helicopters and transports Sea Harriers. RFA Argus is managed and operated by the RFA Service but there is a sizeable Royal Naval Aviation Group embarked. In 1991, during the Gulf War, RFA Argus was used as a Primary Casualty Receiving Ship. The complement is generally about 75 x RFA personnel, 28 x RN personnel and a training group of some 130 RN personnel. In an emergency, the ship could probably carry up to 700 troops.

Forward Repair Ship

	In Service
RFA Diligence	1981

Launched in 1981 and named the Stena Inspector, the ship was originally chartered during the Falklands War and taken into Royal Naval Service as RFA Diligence during 1984. RFA Diligence is a general repair and maintenance ship and capable of providing specialised maintenance support across the fleet. The vessel is particularly useful when Task Forces are operating far from home bases and, in the past, has provided particularly valuable support especially in the Gulf during 1991 and alongside in Split (Croatia) during the past three years.

Landing Ships Logistic

Sir Geraint	1967
Sir Bedivere	1966
Sir Percivale	1967
Sir Tristram	1966 (rebuilt 1985)
Sir Galahad	1988

The five LSLs in service with the RFA are capable of carrying approximately 400 troops and there is a beaching cargo capacity of 3,440 tons. Heavy stores and equipment are carried, including armoured vehicles, and the ships are fitted with bow and stern loading doors and ramps. They are capable of beach landings and the operation of helicopters. During the Falklands Campaign two LSLs sustained heavy damage. RFA Sir Tristram was subsequently redesigned, rebuilt and re-entered service in late 1985. RFA Sir Galahad was later sunk and designated an official War Grave, with a new RFA Sir Galahad entering service in 1988.

Ro-Ro General Cargo Ship

	In Service
Sea Crusader	1996

Sea Crusader entered service in 1996 as a Ro-Ro general cargo vessel having been built to commercial specifications. The vessel is available for use by the Joint Rapid Reaction Force plus general freight duties and there is a requirement for a second vessel (Sea Chieftain). Sea Crusader has 2,300 lane metres of space and a stern ramp capacity of 150 tons. With a complement of 17 and 161 metres in length the vessel is not equipped to enter a war zone.

Royal Maritime Auxiliary Service (RMAS)

The Royal Maritime Auxiliary Service (RMAS) provides the Royal Navy with the wide variety of waterborne services needed at naval bases. Marine Services has taken its present shape during the past 30 years by combining the areas formerly managed by Captains of Dockyards, senior victualling, armament supply, and naval stores officers. This was followed by the amalgamation in 1975 of the separate Marine Services such as ocean tugs, Admiralty cable ships, trials vessels, and the Mooring and Salvage service into the present organisation.

The RMAS operates about 400 vessels and lighters and is a unified service manned by a civilian staff of some 425 officers and 1,250 junior staff. Tasks include the provision of tugs and pilots for harbour movements, ocean and coastal towing; moorings, salvage and diving operations, the transport of personnel, fuel, water, stores and ammunition; torpedo recovery, degaussing, Fleet trials support, tank cleaning, pollution control, and marine range safety duties.

RMAS vessels are allocated to the UK Naval bases at Portsmouth, Devonport, Rosyth, Portland, the Clyde, Pembroke Dock, Kyle of Lochalsh and Gibraltar. RMAS vessels are easily recognised by their buff-coloured funnels and superstructure and their black hulls, which have an all-round white riband at deck level. They fly the blue ensign, which is defaced in the fly by a yellow anchor above two yellow wavy lines.

Support operations are carried out mainly in UK waters with occasional overseas deployments ranging from the Mediterranean to the Falklands.

Fleet Air Arm

The Fleet Air Arm provides the air support for the Royal Navy and the Royal Marines. Harrier Squadrons are embarked on the three carriers HMS Ark Royal, HMS Illustrious and HMS Invincible, as are detachments of the airborne early warning and anti-submarine Sea King helicopter squadrons. The majority of RN ships of the destroyer/frigate type have their own anti-submarine/anti-ship Lynx aircraft that also serve a vital fleet communications role. Whilst not strictly part of the Fleet Air Arm, the Royal Marines 3 Cdo Bde Air Sqn is a Royal Naval organisation that provides communications and anti-tank helicopter support for Commando forces operating ashore. The overall current Fleet Air Arm basic structure is as follows:

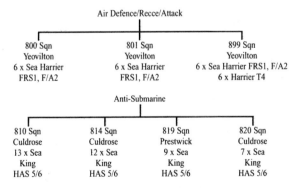

Air Defence/Recce/Attack

800 Sqn	801 Sqn	899 Sqn
Yeovilton	Yeovilton	Yeovilton
6 x Sea Harrier	6 x Sea Harrier	6 x Sea Harrier FRS1, F/A2
FRS1, F/A2	FRS1, F/A2	6 x Harrier T4

Anti-Submarine

810 Sqn	814 Sqn	819 Sqn	820 Sqn
Culdrose	Culdrose	Prestwick	Culdrose
13 x Sea	12 x Sea	9 x Sea	7 x Sea
King	King	King	King
HAS 5/6	HAS 5/6	HAS 5/6	HAS 5/6

Aircraft in these squadrons are often deployed in flights of single or multiple aircraft.

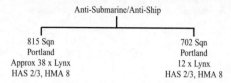

Anti-Submarine/Anti-Ship

815 Sqn	702 Sqn
Portland	Portland
Approx 38 x Lynx	12 x Lynx
HAS 2/3, HMA 8	HAS 2/3, HMA 8

The majority of 815 Squadron's aircraft are at sea on board RN Frigates/Destroyers. Of the squadron total about 25-30 aircraft are probably assigned to ships at any one time.

Commando Air Assault

845 Sqn	846 Sqn	848 Sqn
Yeovilton	Yeovilton	Yeovilton
10 x Sea King	10 x Sea King	Training/Special Tasks
HC4	HC4	9 x Sea King HC4

In addition to the above the Fleet Air Arm has the following:

Airborne Early Warning	849 Sqn	Culdrose	8 x Sea King AEW2
Fleet Support & SAR	771 Sqn	Culdrose	5 x Sea King Mk5
	772 Sqn	Portland	6 x Sea King Mk4
3 Cdo Bde Air Sqn		Yeovilton	7 x Gazelle & Lynx Mk7
Aircrew Training	750 Sqn	Culdrose	13 x Jetstream T2/3

Sea Harrier

In Service With:

800 Sqn	6 x Sea Harrier FRS1, F/A2GR7	RNAS Yeovilton
801 Sqn	6 x Sea Harrier FRS1, F/A2GR7	RNAS Yeovilton
899 Sqn	12 x Sea Harrier FRS1, F/A2GR7	RNAS Yeovilton
	4 x Sea Harrier T4	RNAS Yeovilton

F/A2 (FRS2) Crew 1; Length Overall 14.17m; Wingspan 7.70m; Height 3.71m; Max Level Speed 1185 km/h (736 mph) at low level; Max Take-Off Weight approx 11,880 kg (26,200 lbs); Armament - Able to carry bombs, rockets, guns, missiles and flares attached to 4 x wing weapon pylons and 1 x underfuselage weapon pylon; Engine 1 x RollsRoyce Pegasus Mk 2 vectored thrust turbofan; Ferry Attack Radius 463 kms (288 miles).

In service with the Royal Navy since 1979, the Sea Harrier has been improved and updated to cope with the technological advances that the changing threat has posed. The aircraft remains the most advanced ship-borne Short Take Off and Vertical Landing (STOVL) aircraft in the world.

The aircraft has a maritime figher/reconnaissance/strike role and proved itself as an effective, flexible and reliable aircraft in the Falklands Campaign, where 29 aircraft flew over 2,300 sorties and destroyed 22 enemy aircraft in air-to-air combat without loss. The original version in Royal Naval Service was the FRS1 with the newer F/A2 (FRS2) variant entering service in 1994. The FRS2 differs from the earlier model in that it has a Blue Vixen look-down/shoot-down radar combined with the fire and forget Advanced Medium Range Air-to-Air Missile (AMRAAM) which allows the aircraft to engage targets beyond visual range. In addition, the Sea Eagle (anti-ship missile) and laser-guided bombs can be carried.

The STOVL capability of the Sea Harrier enables the aircraft to operate from the flight deck of an aircraft carrier without the use of catapult-assisted take-off and arrester-wire equipment. "Ski-jump" launching ramps that improve the aircraft's take-off performance are fitted to all three of the Royal Navy's aircraft carriers.

By the end of 1998, 18 x new F/A2 aircraft will have entered service and 31 of the remaining aircraft will have received their mid-life update to bring them up to the F/A2 standard. The T4 is a two seat trainer version of the Harrier.

Expect a Sea Harrier Squadron to have 9 established crews.

Sea King
In Service With:

810 Sqn	Sea King HAS 5/6	13
814 Sqn	Sea King HAS 5/6	12
819 Sqn	Sea King HAS 5/6	9
820 Sqn	Sea King HAS 5/6	7
849 Sqn	Sea King AEW 2	9
845 Sqn	Sea King HC4	10
846 Sqn	Sea King HC4	10
848 Sqn	Sea King HC4	9
771 Sqn	Sea King Mk5	5
772 Sqn	Sea King Mk4	6

HAS Mk 5/6: Crew 2 on flight deck and two in cabin; Fuselage Length 17.01m; Width 3.78m; Height 4.72m; Weight (empty) 6,201 kg; Max Take-Off Weight 9,525 kg; Rotor Diameter 18.9m; Cruising Speed 208 km h (129 mph) at sea level; Service Ceiling 1,220m; Mission Radius (with 2 hours on station and carrying 3 x torpedoes) 231 kms (144 miles); Engines 2 x Rolls Royce Gnome H.1400 1T turboshafts mounted side by side above the cabin; Armament such as 7.62mm MG or 40mm Grenade Launchers can be fitted where appropriate.

The Westland Sea King is a licence built version of the US Sikorsky S-61 and the Royal Navy's HAS Mark 1 aircraft's first flight was in 1969. Since that time, the aircraft has been extensively upgraded and passed through a series of Marks.

The current situation is that the Royal Navy operates the HAS Mk 5/6 in the anti-submarine role. The aircraft can remain on station for long periods up to 100 miles from the ship and can search for submarine targets using either its own sonar-bouys or those dropped by maritime patrol aircraft such as Nimrods. Targets that have been located are then attacked with torpedoes or depth charges.

The AEW 2 is used for airborne early warning and is a Sea King HAS Mark 2 fitted with a Thorn EMI Search Water radar carried in a radardome that can be swivelled down underneath the aircraft for operational searches. A detachment of three AEW 2 aircraft generally deploys with each aircraft carrier.

The Sea King HC4 (Commando) is a tactical military helicopter capable of transporting 28 fully equipped troops or 6,000 lbs (2,720 kg) as an internal load. Carrying 28 troops the aircraft has a range of about 246 miles (396 km). The first HC4 deliveries were made to the Royal Navy in 1979.

The Mk 5 aircraft in service with 771 Sqn are SAR aircraft (Search & Rescue). RN SAR aircraft are stationed at Prestwick, Culdrose and Portland.

Lynx

In Service With:

815 Sqn	Lynx HAS 3, HMA 8	38
3 Cdo Bde Air Sqn	Lynx Mk 7	6

Crew - 2 On the flight-deck and up to 2 mission crew in the fuselage; Length Fuselage 11.92m: Height 3.2m: Rotor Diameter 12.8m: Max Speed 144 mph (232 km h) at sea level: Ferry Range 1,046 km (650 miles) with max internal and external fuel tanks; Engines 2 Rolls Royce Gem Mk 42 Turboshafts; Weight (max take-off) 4,876 kg (10,750 lbs);

Lynx aircraft are at sea with all frigates and destroyers to provide anti-surface surveillance and anti-submarine warfare (ASW) capabilities. With the introduction into service of the first of the upgraded 44 x HAS 3, HMA 8 aircraft in late 1994 the Lynx in Royal Naval service has been turned from an anti-submarine helicopter into a dedicated maritime attack aircraft. Capable of carrying anti-submarine torpedoes (range 10 km) and anti-ship Sea Skua missiles (range 20 km) the HMA 8 is capable of integrating its navigational, communications and fighting systems through a 1553B databus.

Typical combat mission profiles in the anti-submarine role could be a patrol out to 60 miles, a two hour loiter in the search area carrying torpedoes and smoke markers etc and return.

EH 101 Merlin HAS Mk1

Service Ceiling 4,572 m; Range 550 n miles (1,019 km); Sensors; GEC-Marconi Blue Kestrel 5000 radar, Thomson Marconi Flash AQS 960 dipping sonar, GEC-Marconi sonobuoy acoustic processor AQS-903, Racal Orange Reaper ESM; Weapons: ASW - 4 x Stingray torpedoes or Mk 11 Mod 3 depth bombs plus anti-ship missiles.

The Royal Navy has 44 x EH 101 Merlin ASW helicopters on order in a contract worth £1.5 billion. The "in service date" is 1998 and by the early part of the next decade the Merlin should have replaced the ASW Sea Kings and some of the ASW Lynx in Royal Naval service. Extensive sea trials were held on HMS Iron Duke in 1993 and the first aircraft came off the production line in 1996.

During 1998, about 60 hours of flight trials and 20 hours of mission system trials will be carried out at Yeovil by pilots and engineers from the Defence Research and Evaluation Agency after which the aircraft will "enter service" with the RN's Intensive Flight Trials Unit at RNAS Culdrose. Current plans are for all 44 Merlins to be delivered by 2001 and by mid-1998, approximately 12 aircraft were flying.

<u>**Royal Naval Missiles**</u>

Exocet MM38

Length 5.21m; Diameter 0.45m; Total Weight 750 kg; Range 45 km.

Exocet MM38 is a medium range surface-launched anti-ship missile and is carried in the Type 22 Batch 2 frigates. The guidance system is active radar terminal homing.

Sea Wolf

Length 1.91m; Diameter 0.18m; Total Weight 79.8 kg; Range 6/7,000 m; Altitude 3/4000m.

Sea Wolf is a ship-based, surface-to-air missile designed for the defence of point targets. This is a highly efficient system thought to be capable of dealing with aircraft, missiles and even artillery rounds. The guidance system is semi-automatic command to line of sight with radar and/or infra-red missile and target tracking.

Sea Skua

Length 2.85m; Diameter 0.22m; Total Weight 147 kg; Range 20 km approx.

Sea Skua is a short-range, anti-ship missile that has been in Royal Naval service since 1982. The missile is currently carried as the main armament of the Lynx aircraft flying from RN destroyers/frigates. The guidance system is semi-active terminal homing.

Sea Dart

Length 4.40m; Diameter 0.42m; Total Weight 549 kg; Range 80 km+ approx.

Sea Dart is a surface-to-air missile system with a long range (probably in excess of 80 kms) and employs a two-stage system with a primary booster rocket powering the warhead and ramjet on their way to the target. There is a limited surface-to-surface capability out to a range of about 28 km and the guidance system is a semi-active homing radar.

Harpoon

Length 3.84m: Diameter 0.343m: Total Weight 526 kg: Warhead Weight 225 kg: Range 110 km.

Harpoon, manufactured by McDonnel-Douglas of the USA, is an extremely powerful anti-shipping missile that is fitted to the Type 22 and Type 23 Frigates. The Sub Harpoon (UGM-84A) is fitted to the Trafalgar and Swiftsure Class submarines. The latest versions of this missile have extremely sophisticated electronic counter measures (ECM), and the ability to fly a sea-skimming course on a dog-leg path through three pre-programmed way points. The warhead is extremely powerful and a hit from Harpoon is almost certain to result in the destruction or disablement of a major surface vessel.

Other Missiles

Missiles in Royal Naval Service such as AMRAAM, Sea Eagle and Sidewinder are also in RAF service and the relevant entries are in the RAF Section (Part 4)

The Royal Marines

Although the Royal Marines (RM) are part of the Royal Navy, they are trained and equipped for warfare or operations on land, and because of their role it is very likely that they could be involved in operations and exercises with allied marine and army units. The Royal Marines number approximately 500 officers and 5,500 men and, until recently, the primary task for the bulk of the Corps was the reinforcement of Norway and NATO's Northern Flank, should a threat develop in that area. Events have moved on since the end of the Cold War, and of late, the Corps appears to have reverted to its traditional role of being ready for operations anywhere in the world.

The Royal Marines also have detachments on 12 ships at sea and a number of smaller units worldwide with widely differing tasks. However, the bulk of the manpower of the Royal Marines is grouped in battalion-sized organisations known as Commandos (Cdo). There are 3 Commando Groups and they are part of a larger formation known as 3 Commando Brigade (3 Cdo Bde).

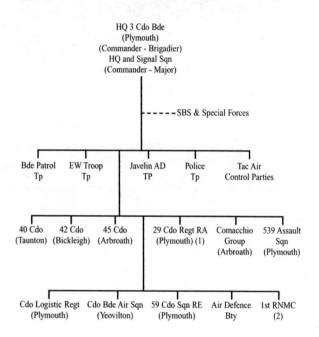

Note:
(1) 29 Cdo Regt RA has one battery stationed at Arbroath with 45 Cdo.
(2) 1st Bn The Royal Netherlands Marine Corps is part of 3 Cdo Bde for NATO assigned tasks.

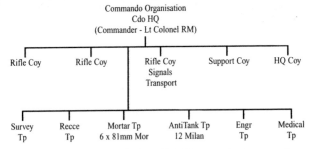

Commando Organisation
Cdo HQ
(Commander - Lt Colonel RM)

- Rifle Coy
- Rifle Coy
- Rifle Coy / Signals / Transport
- Support Coy
- HQ Coy

- Survey Tp
- Recce Tp
- Mortar Tp / 6 x 81mm Mor
- AntiTank Tp / 12 Milan
- Engr Tp
- Medical Tp

Note: A troop (Tp) equates to an army platoon. Each rifle company has three troops. A Royal Marine rifle company is generally commanded by a Captain RM.

Royal Marine Listing

Headquarters Royal Marines	-	Portsmouth
HQ 3 Commando Brigade	-	Plymouth (Stonehouse)
3 Commando Bde HQ & Signal Sqn	-	Plymouth (Stonehouse)
3 Commando Bde Air Sqn	-	RNAS Yeovilton
40 Commando	-	Taunton
42 Commando	-	Plymouth (Bickleigh)
45 Commando	-	Arbroath (Condor)
Commando Logistic Regiment	-	Plymouth (Marsh Mills)
539 Assault Sqn	-	Plymouth (Turnchapel)
Comacchio Group	-	Arbroath (Condor)
Commando Training Centre	-	Lympstone
Royal Marines Stonehouse	-	Plymouth
Royal Marines Poole	-	Poole
Amphibious Training & Trials Unit	-	Bideford

There are Royal Marine Reserve Units in London, Bristol, Birkenhead, Glasgow and Newcastle Upon Tyne.

Special Boat Service (SBS)
This organisation is the Naval equivalent of the Army's SAS (Special Air Service). Personnel are all volunteers from the mainstream Royal Marines and vacancies are few with competition for entry fierce. Generally speaking only about 30% of volunteers manage to complete the entry course and qualify. The SBS specialises in mounting clandestine operations against targets at sea, in rivers or harbours and against occupied coastlines.

Comacchio Company
This specialist company was formed in 1980, and has the task of guarding the UK's oil rigs and other associated installations from a variety of threats - in particular terrorist attacks.

43

THE STRATEGIC DEFENCE REVIEW 1998 (SDR) ON THE NAVAL FORCES OF THE U.K.

General

The UK MoD's 1998 SDR was launched by the Secretary of State For Defence, George Robertson at a press conference on 28th May 1998. The Study was originally commissioned during May 1997 and, during the following 12 months, inputs were invited from a variety of interested parties. Amongst these were:

MoD Central Staffs	DERA
Army Staff	Expert Panel
Air Staff	Public Submissions
Naval Staff	Seminars
Individual Service Personnel	Allies
Civil Servants	Trade Unions
PJHQ	Parliament
Procurement Executive	Cabinet Office
Environmental Groups	Industry
Local Authorities	Scientific Community
Foreign & Commonwealth Office	

The major aspects of the 1998 SDR that will be of particular interest to the Royal Navy is as follows:

Nuclear Capability

The UK Government is committed to maintaining nuclear weapons as the ultimate guarantee of the country's security. Nuclear weapons will continue to be based on the Royal Navy's Trident submarine fleet (SSBN) and the fourth and last submarine of the present fleet, HMS Vengeance will be launched later in 1998. A fleet of four Trident equipped submarines will allow the Royal Navy to maintain continuous deterrent patrols over the lifetime of Trident fleet.

Trident is the UK's only nuclear weapon system remaining in service. The army's Lance missiles and nuclear capable artillery, the Royal Navy's maritime nuclear weapons and the RAF's air-launched nuclear weapons have all been "given up".

What is seen as an "improved strategic environment" means that the UK Government believes that it is possible to reduce holdings of nuclear weapons and it is no longer necessary to have a stockpile of around 300 warheads. The stockpile is therefore being reduced to 200 operationally available warheads. In addition, the 58 missile bodies already purchased are believed to be sufficient to maintain a credible deterrent.

The MoD has further confirmed that there will be one SSBN on patrol at any one time but carrying a reduced load of 48 warheads. The submarine's missiles will not be "targeted" and will be at several days "notice to fire". Over a period of time the current system of having two crews for each submarine will be reduced to one crew, a system that better reflects the reduced operational tempo.

Stocks of fissile materials will be reduced. Current (1998) stocks are 7.6 tonnes of plutonium, 21.9 tonnes of highly enriched uranium and 15,000 tonnes of other forms of uranium. The reduction in warheads will allow 4.4 tonnes of plutonium (including 0.3 tonnes of weapons-grade plutonium) and 9,000 tonnes of highly enriched uranium to be placed under EURATOM (European Atomic Energy Community) safeguards.

The operating costs of the Trident force are estimated to be in the region of £277 million annually over the expected 30 year life cycle of the fleet. The annual breakdown of this cost is as follows:

Manpower	-	£33 million
In-service Support of Submarine	-	£33 million
In-service Support (Nuclear Propulsion)	-	£13 million
In-service Support (Trident Missile System)	-	£47 million
Base/Site Running Costs	-	£61 million
Refit-Maintenance	-	£53 million
Stores and Spares	-	£35 million
In-service Trials	-	£1 million
Dedicated Communications	-	£1 million
Total	-	£277 million

Royal Navy

The review suggests a shift in emphasis during the future from the large open-ocean operations of the 'Cold War' era towards a wide range of operations in littoral areas. Force projection and support to prolonged peace support operations look like being the highest priorities in the short to medium term. This maritime change of emphasis will be reflected in the following changes:

Aircraft Carriers

In the longer term, there are plans to replace the Invincible Class aircraft carriers. These carriers were designed for 'Cold War' anti-submarine operations. These carriers have a small number of Sea Harriers embarked for local air defence and the new emphasis will be on offensive air power. There are plans for two new aircraft carriers of between 30,000-40,000 tons capable of deploying about 50 aircraft including helicopters. As yet no decision has been taken on the type of aircraft that these vessels would deploy but the Joint Strike Fighter, currently being developed in the US would be a strong contender. In the short term, Royal Navy Sea Harriers and Royal Air Force GR7 Harriers will combine in a new force (Joint Force 2000) that will be capable of operating from either land or carrier bases.

Destroyers & Frigates

The destroyer and frigate force will continue to be modernised and a new class of Common New Generation Frigates (Project Horizon) will be introduced into service. However, overall strength of the destroyer and frigate force will fall from 35 to 32. A force of 32 frigates would be capable of sustaining two concurrent medium scale deployments, this being what the government believes is the most demanding requirement the Royal Navy faces.

Attack Submarines
The strength of the nuclear-powered attack submarine force will fall from 12 to 10 vessels in the longer term. Modernisation of the force will continue and all 10 vessels will be equipped with the Tomahawk land attack (conventional) cruise missile. Earlier plans were for seven submarines to be equipped with Tomahawk.

Royal Marines
3 Commando Brigade will be retained in full and the modernisation programme will continue. The helicopter carrier HMS Ocean is in service and, in the future there are plans to procure two landing ships logistic and two landing platform docks to replace current vessels.

Miscellaneous
The mine countermeasures fleet will be increased from 19 to 22 vessels but a previous target of 25 will be cancelled and older vessels paid off.

Plans for the purchase of 44 Merlin anti-submarine helicopters will go ahead and 10 Lynx Mk3 helicopters will be upgraded to Mk 8 standard for operation from the destroyer/frigate force.

Planned modernisation of the Royal Fleet Auxiliary will continue and two auxiliary oilers will be procured to replace existing vessels.

In the medium term these changes should reduce undermanning in the Royal Navy and, once the major manning problems have been resolved, the Navy's regular manpower requirement will be reduced by about 1,400 posts.